Audition Son Female Singers Classical Greats

Ten classical songs and arias ideal for auditions

r

CW00349825

Wise Publications
part of The Music Sales Group
London/New York/Paris/Sydney/Copenhagen/Berlin/Madrid/Tokyo

Notes And Original Texts

Songs are listed alphabetically by title

Dates indicate the first performance of each work

CARO MIO BEN

1878

Music by Giuseppe Giordani

Text by Anon

Caro mio ben, credimi almen,
Senza di te languisce il cor.
Il tuo fedel sospira ognor.
Cessa, crudel, tanto rigor!

RECORDINGS

Cecelia Bartoli on *Cecelia Bartoli: A Portrait,* Decca Music Group Limited (1995)

Lesley Garrett on *Lesley Garrett,* BMG UK & Ireland Ltd. (1998)

Katherine Jenkins on *Premiere,* Universal Classics & Jazz (2004)

CARO NOME (from RIGOLETTO)

1851

Music by Giuseppe Verdi

Libretto by Francesco Maria Piave

Caro nome che il mio cor
Festi primo palpitar,
Le delizie dell' amor
Mi dei sempre rammentar!
Col pensier il mio desir
A te sempre volerà,
E fin l'ultimo sospir,
Caro nome, tuo sarà.

RECORDINGS

Montserrat Caballé on *Montserrat Caballé: The Ultimate Collection,* RCA Classics (1999)

Angela Gheorghiu on *Verdi Heroines,* Decca Music Group Limited (2000)

Maria Callas on *Ultimate Callas,* EMI Classics (2005)

HABANERA (from CARMEN)

1875
Music by Georges Bizet
Libretto by Henri Meilhac and Ludovic Halévy

L'amour est un oiseau rebelle, que nul ne peut apprivoiser.
Et c'est bien en vain qu'on l'appelle, s'il lui convient de refuser.
Rien n'y fait, menace ou prière, l'un parle bien, l'autre se tait;
Et c'est l'autre que je préfère il n'a rien dit; mais il me plaît.
L'amour! L'amour! L'amour! L'amour!

L'amour est enfant de Bohême, il n'a jamais, jamais connu de loi,
Si tu ne m'aime pas, je t'aime, si je t'aime, prend garde à toi!
Si tu ne m'aime pas, si tu ne m'aime pas, je t'aime!
Mais, si je t'aime, si je t'aime, prend garde à toi!
Si tu ne m'aime pas, si tu ne m'aime pas, je t'aime!
Mais, si je t'aime, si je t'aime, prend garde à toi!

L'oiseau que tu croyais surprendre battit de l'aile et s'envola;
L'amour est loin, tu peux l'attendre; tu ne l'attend plus, il est là!
Tout autour de toi vite, vite, il vient, s'en va, puis il revient!
Tu crois le tenir, il t'évite; tu crois l'éviter, il te tient!
L'amour, l'amour, l'amour, l'amour!

RECORDINGS

Denyce Graves on *Voce Di Donna,* Classics/Windham (1999)
Katherine Jenkins on *Premiere,* Universal Classics & Jazz (2004)
Maria Callas on *Maria Callas: The Platinum Collection,* EMI Classics (2005)

PANIS ANGELICUS

1872
Music by César Franck
Text by St. Thomas Aquinas

Panis angelicus, fit panis hominum.
Dat panis coelicus, figuris terminum.
O res mirabilis, manducat Dominum
Pauper et servus et humilis.

RECORDINGS

Cecelia Bartoli on *A Hymn For The World,* Deustche Grammophon (1997)
Charlotte Church on *Voice Of An Angel,* Sony Classics (1999)

THE SILVER SWAN

1612
Music by Orlando Gibbons
Text by Anon

The silver swan who, living, had no note, when death approached, unlocked her silent throat.
Leaning her breast against the reedy shore, thus sung her first and last, and sung no more:
"Farewell all joys, O death come close mine eyes.
More geese than swans now live, more fools than wise."

THE TROUT

1817
Music by Franz Schubert
Text by Christian Friedrich Daniel Schubart

In einem Bächlein helle, da schoß in froher Eil' die launische Forelle vor über wie ein Pfeil.
Ich stand an dem Gestade und sah in süßer Ruh' des muntern Fischleins Bade im klaren Bächlein zu.

Ein Fischer mit der Rute, wohl an dem Ufer stand, und sah's mit klarem Blute, wie sich das Fischlein wand.
So lang dem Wasser Helle, So dacht' ich, nicht gebricht, so fängt er die Forelle Mit seiner Angel nicht.

Doch endlich ward dem Diebe. Die Zeit zu lang er macht das Bächlein tückisch trübe, und eh' ich es gedacht,
So zuckte seine Rute, das Fischlein zappelt d'ran, und ich mit regem Blute sah die Betrogene an.

RECORDINGS

Elisabeth Schumann on *Elisabeth Schumann: Schubert Lieder,* Naxos Historical (2002)
Anne Sophie von Otter on *Schubert: Lieder With Orchestra,* Deutsche Grammophon (2003)

VOI CHE SAPETE (from THE MARRIAGE OF FIGARO)

1786
Music by Wolfgang Amadeus Mozart
Libretto by Lorenzo Da Ponte

Voi, che sapete che cosa è amor, donne, vedete s'io l'ho nel cor!
Quello ch'io provo, vi ridirò; è per me nuovo, capir nol so.

Sento un affetto pien di desir, ch'ora è diletto, ch'ora è martir.
Gelo, e poi sento l'alma avvampar, E in un momento torno a gelar.
Ricerco un bene fuori di me, non so chi il tiene, non so cos'è.

Sospiro e gemo senza voler, palpito e tremo senza saper.
Non trovo pace notte, nè di, ma pur mi piace languir così!

RECORDINGS

Cecelia Bartoli on *Cecelia Bartoli: A Portrait,* Decca Music Group Limited (1995)
Elisabeth Schwarzkopf on *Great Recordings Of The Century: Mozart: Opera Arias,* EMI Classics (2005)
Anne Sophie von Otter on *Mozart: Le Nozze Di Figaro,* Deutsche Grammophon (2005)

WHEN I AM LAID IN EARTH (from DIDO AND AENEAS)

1689

Music by Henry Purcell

Libretto by Nahum Tate

Thy hand, Belinda; darkness shades me; on thy bosom let me rest.

More I would, but Death invades me: Death is now a welcome guest.

When I am laid in earth, may my wrongs create

No trouble in thy breast. Remember me, but ah! Forget my fate.

RECORDINGS

Barbara Bonney on *Barbara Bonney: Fairest Isle,* Decca Music Group Ltd. (2001)

Hayley Westenra on *Odyssey,* Decca Music Group Limited (2005)

WIDMUNG

1840

Music Robert Schumann

Text by Friedrich Rückert

Du meine Seele, du mein Herz, du meine Wonn', o du mein Schmerz,

Du meine Welt, in der ich lebe, mein Himmel du, darein ich schwebe,

O du mein Grab, in das hinab ich ewig meinen Kummer gab.

Du bist die Ruh, du bist der Frieden, du bist vom Himmel mir beschieden.

Dass du mich liebst, macht mich mir wert, dein Blick hat mich vor mir verklärt,

Du hebst mich liebend über mich, mein guter Geist, mein bessres Ich!

RECORDINGS

Kathleen Ferrier on *Kathleen Ferrier Vol.4,* Decca Music Group Limited (1992)

Barbara Bonney on *Robert & Clara Schumann: Lieder,* Decca Music Group Limited (1997)

Jessye Norman on *Jessye Norman Live At Hohenems & Salzburg,* Decca Music Group Limited (2005)

WOHIN

1823

Music by Franz Schubert

Text by Wilhelm Müller

Ich hört' ein Bächlein rauschen wohl aus dem Felsenquell,

Hinab zum Thale rauschen so frisch und wunderhell.

Ich weiss nicht, wie mir wurde, nicht, wer den Rath mir gab,

Ich musste auch hinunter Mit meinem Wanderstab.

Hinunter und immer weiter, und immer dem Bache nach,

Und immer frischer rauschte und immer heller der Bach.

Ist das denn meine Strasse? O Bächlein, sprich, wohin?

Du hast mit deinem Rauschen Mir ganz berauscht den Sinn.

Was sag' ich denn vom Rauschen? Das kann kein Rauschen sein.

Es singen wohl die Nixen dort unten ihren Reihn.

Lass singen, Gesell, lass rauschen, und wand're fröhlich nach!

Es geh'n ja Mühlenräder in jedem klaren Bach.

RECORDINGS

Marian Anderson on *Marian Anderson (Bach, Brahms, Schubert),* Classics/Windham, 1989

Caro Mio Ben

Composed by Giuseppe Giordani

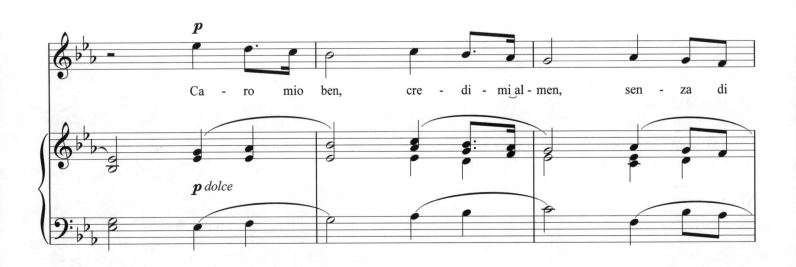

Ca - ro mio ben, cre - di - mi al - men, sen - za di

te lan - gui - sce il cor,_____ ca - ro mio

ben, sen - za di te___ lan - gui - sce il cor.

Il tuo fe - del so - spi - ra o -

- gnor. Ces - sa cru - del,___ tan - to ri - gor! Ces - sa, cru -

- del, tan - to ri - gor,___ tan - to ri - gor! Ca - ro mio

Caro Nome (from "Rigoletto")

Composed by Giuseppe Verdi

Performance Note: The cadenza bars have been fixed into strict tempi to make CD-accompanied performances easier.

-tar, le de - li - zie del - l'a - mor mi dei sem - pre ram - men - tar! Col pen - sier il mio de -

-sir a te sem - pre___ vo - le - rà, e fin l'ul - ti - mo___ so___ spir. ca - ro no - me, tuo___ sa -

col pen - sier il mio de - sir

a te sem-pre vo-le - rà,_____ e fin

dolciss.

l'ul - ti - mo__ mi - o_____ so - spir, ca - ro__

no - - - me,__ tuo__ sa - rà.

Col - pen - sier il_____ mio de - sir

a te sem-pre vo-le - rà,_____

a te_____ vo - le -

-rà, fin l'ul - ti - mo_ so - spir._____ fin_ l'ul - ti - mo_ so - spir,_____

ca - - - - - - - - ro___ no - me,___ tuo sa-

- rà,___ ca - - - - - - - - ro___ no - me, tuo sa-

- rà,___ il mio de - sir a te o - gno - ra

vo - le - rà, fin l'ul - ti - mo so - spi - ro

tuo_____ sa - - - rà.

Gual - tier_____ Mal-

-dè!   Gual -

-tier_____ Mal - dè!   ca - ro no - me, che il mio

14

cor fe - sti pri - mo pal - pi - tar, e fin

l'ul - ti - mo so - spir, ca - ro no - me, tuo sa -

- rà. Gual - tier Mal - dè! Gaul - tier Mal - dè!

perdendosi

Habanera (from "Carmen")

Composed by Georges Bizet

fait, men-ace ou pri-è-re, l'un par-le bien,___ l'au-tre se tait. Et c'est

l'au-tre que je pré-fè-re, il n'a rien dit,___ mais___ il ne

plaît.___ L'a - mour!___ L'a -

- mour!___ L'a - mour!___ L'a -

-mour! L'a-mour est en - fant de Bo - hême, il n'a ja - mais, ja-mais con-nu de

loi. Si tu ne m'ai - mes pas, je t'ai - me, si je t'ai-me, prends garde à

toi!_____ Si tu ne m'ai - mes pas, si tu ne m'ai-mes pas, je

t'ai - me! Mais si je t'ai - me, si je t'ai-mes, prends garde___ à

* For CD-accompanied performances, sing this bar in half-time.

toi!

Si tu ne m'ai - mes pas, si tu ne m'ai-mes pas, je

t'ai - me! Mais si je t'ai - me, si je t'ai - me, prends garde à

cresc.

f

Half-time.

toi!

L'oi - seau que tu croy - ais sur - pren - dre bat - tit de l'aile___ et___ s'en - vo -

- la. L'a - mour est loin, tu peux l'at - ten - dre; tu ne l'at - tends___ plus,_ il est

là! Tout au - tour de toi vi - te, vi - te, il vient, s'en va,___ puis_ il re -

-vient. Tu crois le te-nir, il t'é -vi-te, tu crois l'é - vi - ter, il te

tient!_____ L'a - mour!_____ L'a -

- mour!_____ L'a - mour!_____ L'a -

-mour! L'a-mour est en - fant de Bo-hême, il n'a ja - mais, ja-mais con - nu de

loi. Si tu ne m'ai - mes pas, je t'ai - me, si je t'ai - me, prends garde à

toi!_____ Si tu ne m'ai - mes pas, si tu ne m'ai - mes pas, je

cresc. *f* *pp* *cresc.* *mf*

t'ai - me! Mais si je t'ai - me, si je t'ai - mes, prends garde__ à

toi!_____

ff

* Half-time.

22

Si tu ne m'ai - mes pas, si

tu ne m'ai - mes pas, je t'ai - me! Mais si je

t'ai - me, si je t'ai - me, prends garde à_____ toi!_____

cresc.

f

pp

cresc.

f

pp

f

mf

3

* Half-time.

Panis Angelicus

Composed by César Franck

Pau - per, pau - per, ser - vus et hu - mi - lis.

Pa - nis an - ge - li - cus fit pa - nis ho - mi - num.

Dat pa - nis coe - li - cus fi - gu - ris ter - mi - num.

The Silver Swan

Composed by Orlando Gibbons

last, and_ sang no more. Fare - well all joys, O

death, come close mine eyes. More geese than swans now live, more_ fools than

wise! Fare - well all joys. O death, come close mine

eyes. More geese than swans now live, more_ fools than wise!

rit.

The Trout

Composed by Franz Schubert

-rel - le vor ü - ber___ wie ein Pfeil.
Blu - te, wie sich das___ Fisch-lein wand.

Ich stand an dem_ Ges-
So lang dem Was - ser_

-ta - de und sah in süß - er__ Ruh'
Hel - le, so dacht' ich, nicht ge - bricht,

des munt - ern Fisch-leins
so fängt er die Fo -

Ba - de im klar - en Bäch-lein zu.
-rel - le mit sein - er An - gel nicht.

Des munt - ern Fisch - leins__
So fängt_ er die__ Fo -

Ba - de im klar - en Bäch-lein zu.
-rel - le mit sein - er An - gel nicht.

2. Ein   3. Doch

end - lich ward dem Die - be. Die Zeit zu lang.

Er macht das Bäch - lein tüch - isch trü - be, und eh'_____ ich es ge -

- dacht. So zuck - te sei - ne Ru - te, das Fisch - lein, das

32

Fisch - lein zap - pelt d'ran, und ich mit reg - em

Blu - te sah die Be - trog' - ne an. Und ich__ mit reg - em__

Blu - te sah die Be - trog' - ne an.

Voi Che Sapete
(from "Le Nozze Di Figaro")

Composed by Wolfgang Amadeus Mozart

don - ne, ve - de - te,____ s'io l'ho___ nel___ cor.

Quel - lo ch'io pro - vo, vi_____ ri - di - rò;____

è per me nuo - vo, ca - pir nol so.

Sen - to un af - fet - to pien di de - sir,____

ch'o - ra è di - let - to, ch'o - ra è mar - tir.

Ge - lo, e poi sen - to l'al - ma av - vam - par.

E in un mo - men - to tor - no a ge - lar.

Ri - cer - co un be - ne fuo - ri di me,

non so chi il tie - ne, non so cos' - è. So-spi-ro e ge - mo sen-za vo - ler; pal - i-to e tre - mo sen-za sa - per. Non tro-vo pa-ce not - te, nè di, ma pur mi pia - ce lan - guir co - sì. Voi, che sa - pe - te che co - sa è a-

-mor, don - ne ve - de - te,

s'io l'ho nel cor. Don - ne, ve - de - te,____

s'io l'ho nel cor, don - ne, ve - de - te,____

s'io l'ho__ nel__ cor.

When I Am Laid In Earth
(from "Dido And Aeneas")

Composed by Henry Purcell

* First 3 bars: Accompaniment altered for ease of CD-accompanied performance.

When I am laid,_____ am laid_____ in earth, may my wrongs_____ cre - ate no trou - ble, no trou - ble in thy breast.

When I am laid,_____ am

laid _____ in earth, may my wrongs _____ cre-

-ate no trou - ble, no trou - ble in thy

breast. Re - mem - ber me,

re - mem - ber me, but

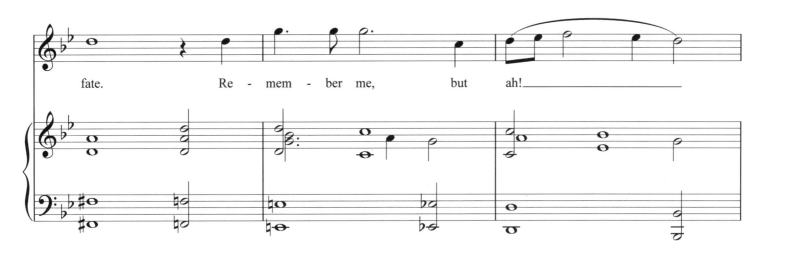

fate.   Re - mem - ber me,   but   ah!_____

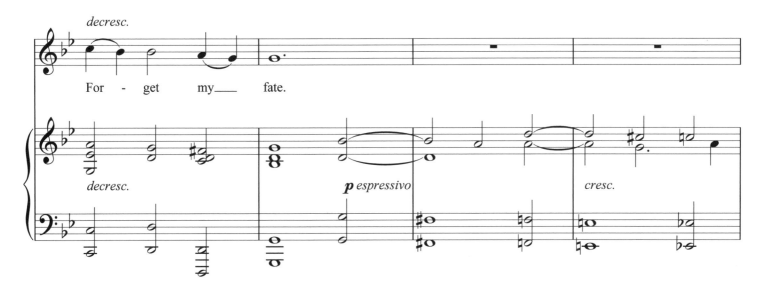

For - get my__ fate.

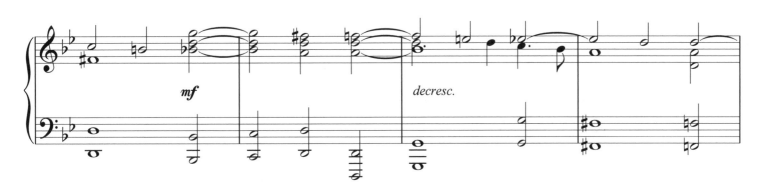

Widmung
Composed by Robert Schumann

du, da-rein ich schwe - be, o du mein Grab, in das hin-

-ab ich e - wig mei-ne Kum - mer gab!

Poco più mosso ♩ = 63

Du bist die Ruh', du bist der

Frie - den, du bist vom Him - mel

45

mir_____ be - schie - den. Dass du mich liebst, macht mich mir

werth,_____ dein Blick hat mich vor mir ver- klart,_____ du hebst mich

A tempo primo ♩ = 50

lie - bend ü - ber mich, mein gu - ter Geist, mein bess' res

Ich! Du mei-ne See - le, du mein Herz, du mei-ne

46

Wonn', o du mein Schmerz, du mei-ne Welt, in der ich

le - be, mein Him - mel du, da - rein ich schwe - be, mein gu - ter

Geist, mein bess' - res Ich!

Wohin?

Composed by Franz Schubert

frisch und wun - der - hell. Ich weiss nicht, wie mir

wur - de, nicht wer den Rath mir gab, ich

muss - te auch hin - un - ter mit mei - nem Wan - der -

- stab, ich muss - te auch hin - un - ter mit

meinem Wan - der - stab. Hin - un - ter und im - mer

wei - ter, und im - mer dem Ba - che nach; und

im - mer fri - scher rasch - te und im - mer hel - ter der

Bach, und im - mer fri - scher rausch - ter und

cresc.

im - mer___ hel - ter der Bach.   Ist

pp

das denn mei - ne Stra - sse?   O Bäch - lein, sprich, wo -

- hin?   Wo - hin?___ sprich, wo - hin?___   Du

hast mit dei - nem Rau - schen mir ganz be - rauscht den

Sinn, du hast mir dei - nem Rau - schen mir

ganz be rauscht den Sinn. Was sag' ich denn vom

Rau - schen? Das kann kein Rau - schen sein. Es

sin - gen wohl die Ni - xen dort un - ten ih - ren

pp

Reih'n, es sin - gen wohl die Ni - xen dort un - ten ih - ren Reih'n. Lass sin - gen, Ge - sell, lass rau - schen, und wan - d're fröh - lich nach, es geh'n ja Müh - len - rä - der in je - dem kla - ren

Bach,_____ es geh'n ja Müh - len - rä - der in___ je - dem kla - ren___ Bach. Lass__ sin - gen, Ge - sell,__ lass__

dim.

ran - schen, und__ wan - d're fröh - lich__ nach, fröh - lich__

nach, fröh - lich nach._____

1 2 3 4 5 6 7 8 9

Published by
Wise Publications
8/9 Frith Street,
London W1D 3JB, UK.

Exclusive Distributors:
Music Sales Limited
Distribution Centre, Newmarket Road,
Bury St Edmunds, Suffolk IP33 3YB, UK.
Music Sales Corporation
257 Park Avenue South,
New York, NY10010, USA.

Music Sales Pty Limited
120 Rothschild Avenue,
Rosebery, NSW 2018,
Australia.

Order No. AM984632
ISBN 1-84609-326-0
This book © Copyright 2006 Wise Publications,
a division of Music Sales Limited.

Music arranged by Derek Jones.
Music processed by Paul Ewers Music Design.
Cover photograph courtesy RB/Redferns.
Printed in the EU.

CD tracks mixed and mastered by Jonas Persson.
Backing tracks by Paul Honey.
Piano by Tau Wey (recorded at Marc Angelo Studios).

CD Track Listing

CD Track 1
Caro Mio Ben
Music: Page 6

CD Track 2
Caro Nome
Music: Page 9

CD Track 3
Habanera
Music: Page 16

CD Track 4
Panis Angelicus
Music: Page 24

CD Track 5
The Silver Swan
Music: Page 28

CD Track 6
The Trout
Music: Page 30

CD Track 7
Voi Che Sapete
Music: Page 34

CD Track 8
When I Am Laid In Earth
Music: Page 39

CD Track 9
Widmung
Music: Page 44

CD Track 10
Wohin?
Music: Page 48

To remove your CD from the plastic sleeve,
lift the small lip to break the perforations.
Replace the disc after use for convenient storage.